# play guitar with...
# blues legends

GW00684695

**Wise Publications**
**London/New York/Paris/Sydney/Copenhagen/Madrid/Tokyo**

**Music Sales Limited**
8-9 Frith Street,
London W1V 5TZ, England.
**Music Sales Pty Limited**
120 Rothschild Avenue,
Rosebery, NSW 2018, Australia.

Order No. AM958507
ISBN 0-7119-8191-4
This book © Copyright 2000
by Wise Publications

Music arranged by Martin Shellard
(except 'The Thrill Is Gone' by Arthur Dick)
Music processed by Andrew Shiels
Cover photographs courtesy of
Redferns

Printed in the United Kingdom by
Caligraving Limited, Thetford, Norfolk.

CD programmed and recorded by Martin Shellard
All guitars by Martin Shellard
(except 'The Thrill Is Gone' by Arthur Dick)

## Your Guarantee of Quality

As publishers, we strive to produce
every book to the highest commercial standards.
The music has been freshly engraved and the book has
been carefully designed to minimise awkward page turns
and to make playing from it a real pleasure.
Particular care has been given to specifying acid-free,
neutral-sized paper made from pulps which have not been
elemental chlorine bleached. This pulp is from farmed
sustainable forests and was produced with
special regard for the environment.
Throughout, the printing and binding have been planned
to ensure a sturdy, attractive publication which
should give years of enjoyment.
If your copy fails to meet our high standards,
please inform us and we will gladly replace it.

**www.musicsales.com**

Music Sales' complete catalogue describes thousands of titles
and is available in full colour sections by subject, direct from
Music Sales Limited. Please state your areas of interest
and send a cheque/postal order for £1.50 for postage to:
Music Sales Limited, Newmarket Road,
Bury St. Edmunds, Suffolk IP33 3YB.

# guitar tablature explained

Guitar music can be notated three different ways: on a musical stave, in tablature, and in rhythm slashes

**RHYTHM SLASHES** are written above the stave. Strum chords in the rhythm indicated. Round noteheads indicate single notes.

**THE MUSICAL STAVE** shows pitches and rhythms and is divided by lines into bars. Pitches are named after the first seven letters of the alphabet.

**TABLATURE** graphically represents the guitar fingerboard. Each horizontal line represents a string, and each number represents a fret.

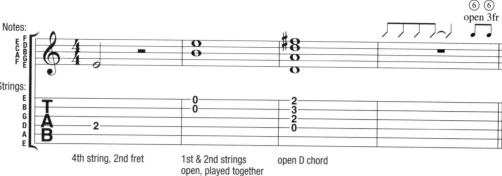

4th string, 2nd fret    1st & 2nd strings open, played together    open D chord

# definitions for special guitar notation

**SEMI-TONE BEND:** Strike the note and bend up a semi-tone (1/2 step).

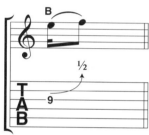

**BEND & RELEASE:** Strike the note and bend up as indicated, then release back to the original note.

**HAMMER-ON:** Strike the first (lower) note with one finger, then sound the higher note (on the same string) with another finger by fretting it without picking.

**NATURAL HARMONIC:** Strike the note while the fret-hand lightly touches the string directly over the fret indicated.

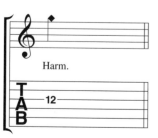

**WHOLE-TONE BEND:** Strike the note and bend up a whole-tone (whole step).

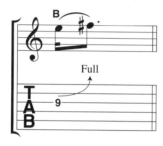

**BEND & RESTRIKE:** Strike the note and bend as indicated then restrike the string where the symbol occurs.

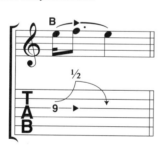

**PULL-OFF:** Place both fingers on the notes to be sounded. Strike the first note and without picking, pull the finger off to sound the second (lower) note.

**PICK SCRAPE:** The edge of the pick is rubbed down (or up) the string, producing a scratchy sound.

**GRACE NOTE BEND:** Strike the note and bend as indicated. Play the first note as quickly as possible.

**PRE-BEND:** Bend the note as indicated, then strike it.

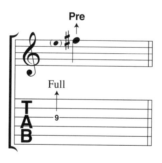

**LEGATO SLIDE (GLISS):** Strike the first note and then slide the same fret-hand finger up or down to the second note. The second note is not struck.

**PALM MUTING:** The note is partially muted by the pick hand lightly touching the string(s) just before the bridge.

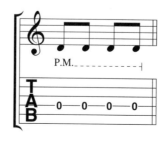

**QUARTER-TONE BEND:** Strike the note and bend up a 1/4 step.

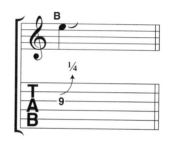

**PRE-BEND & RELEASE:** Bend the note as indicated. Strike it and release the note back to the original pitch.

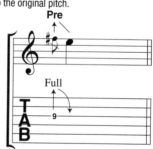

**SHIFT SLIDE (GLISS & RESTRIKE):** Same as legato slide, except the second note is struck.

**MUFFLED STRINGS:** A percussive sound is produced by laying the fret hand across the string(s) without depressing, and striking them with the pick hand.

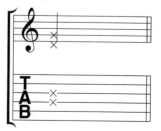

**NOTE:** The speed of any bend is indicated by the music notation and tempo.

# couldn't stand the weather

**Words & Music by Stevie Ray Vaughan**

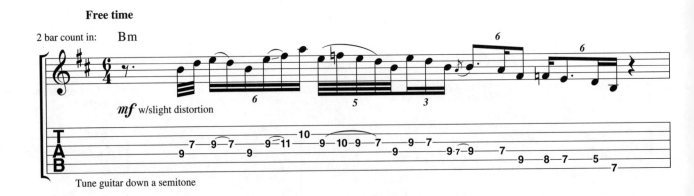

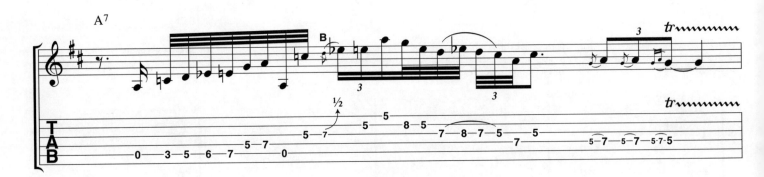

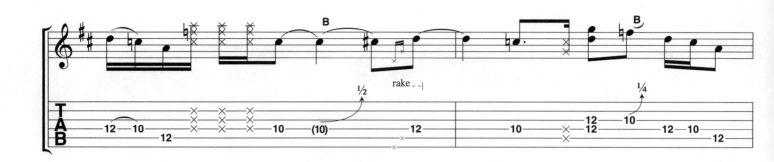
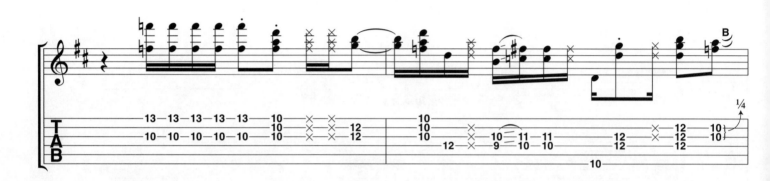
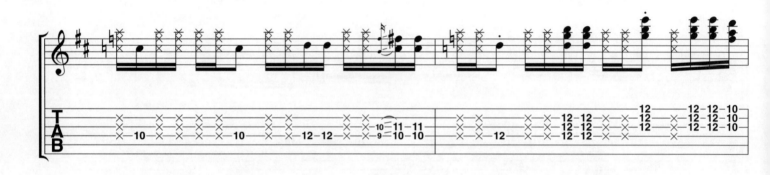
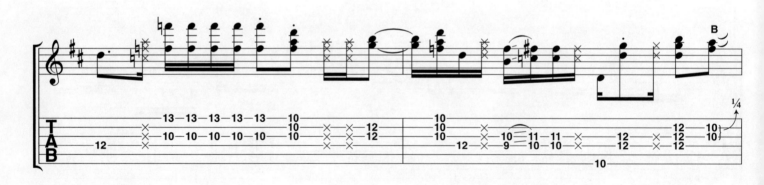
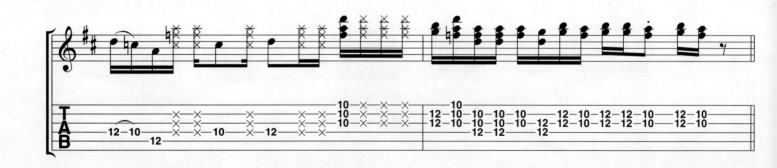

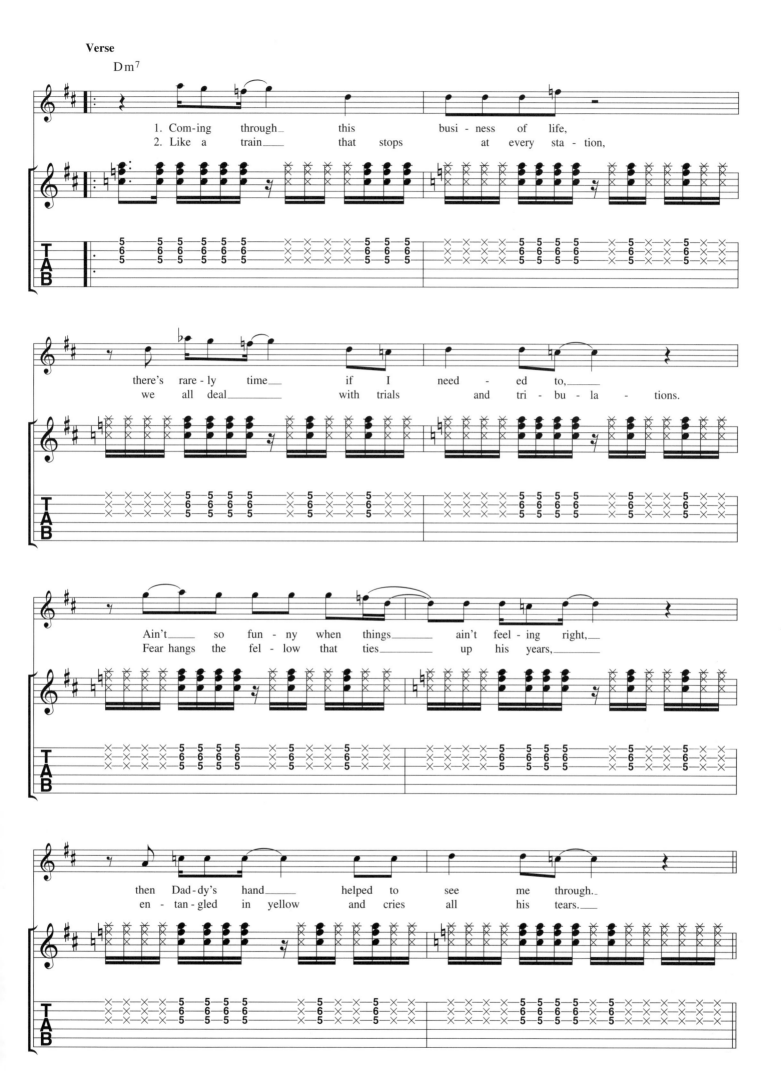

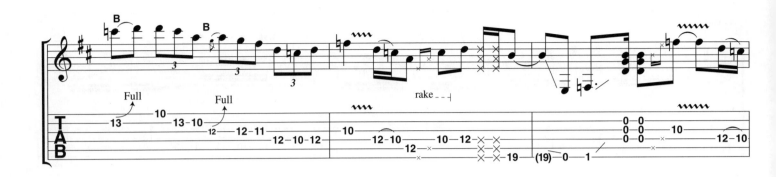

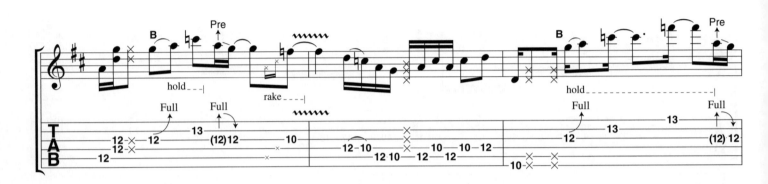

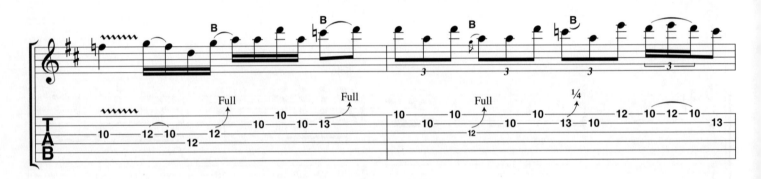

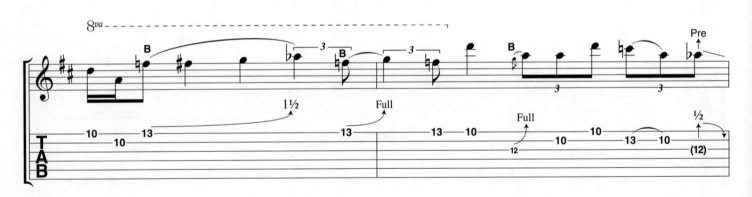

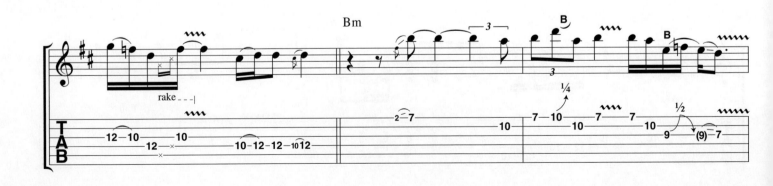

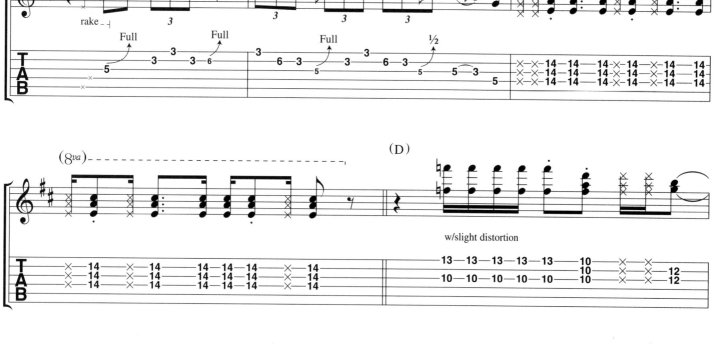

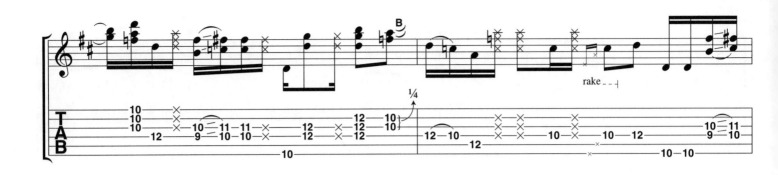
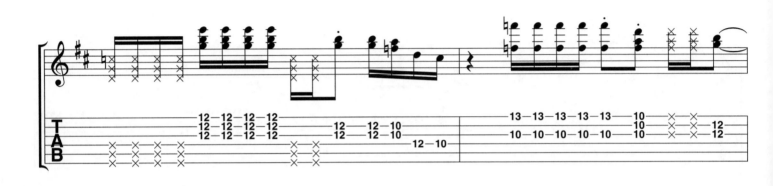
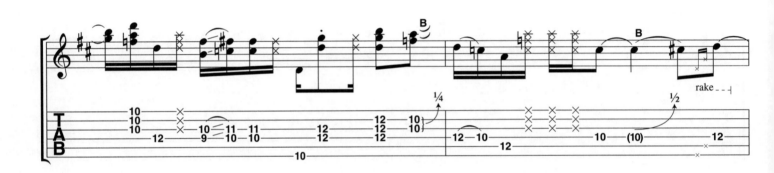
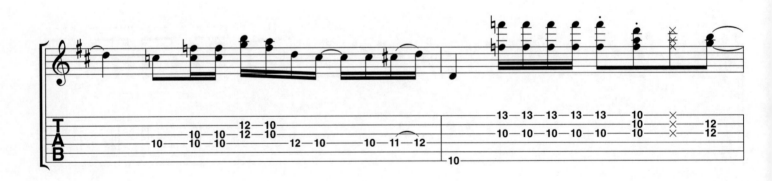
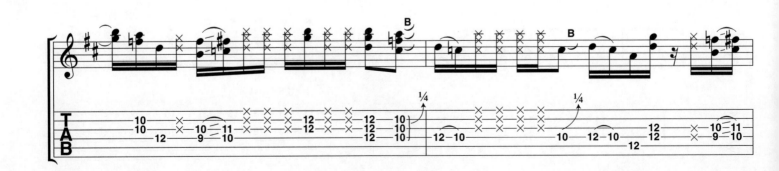

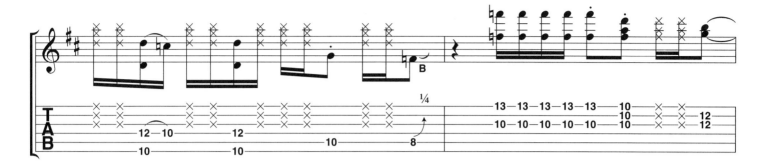

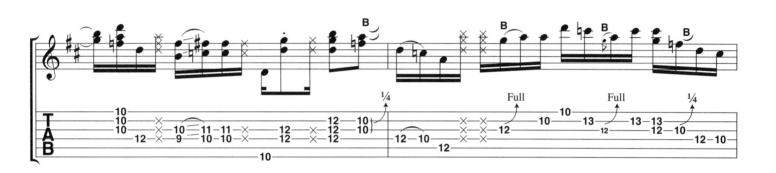

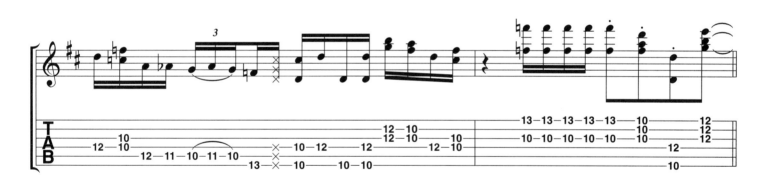

**Free time**

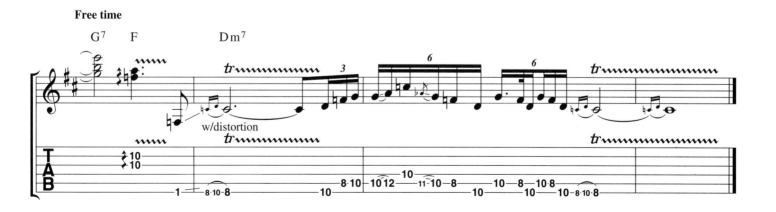

# crossroads blues

**Words & Music by Robert Johnson**

**Intro**

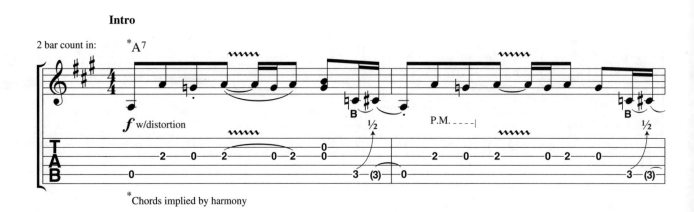

*Chords implied by harmony

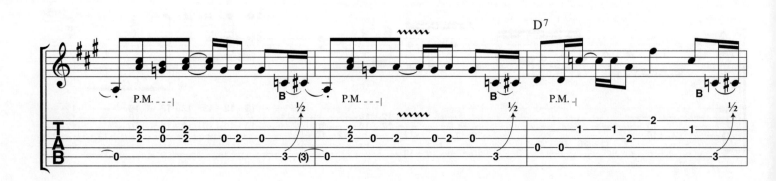

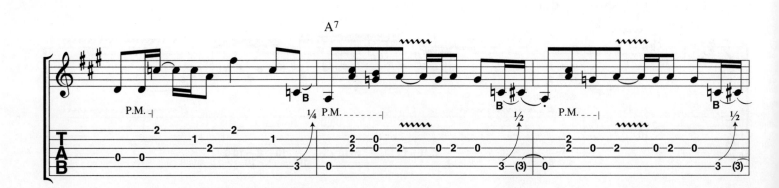

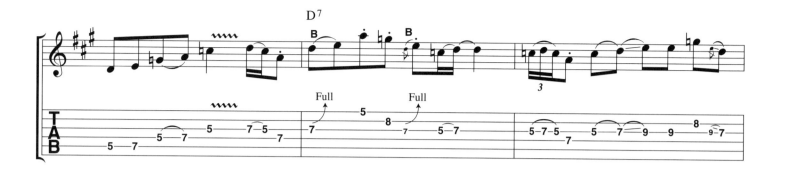

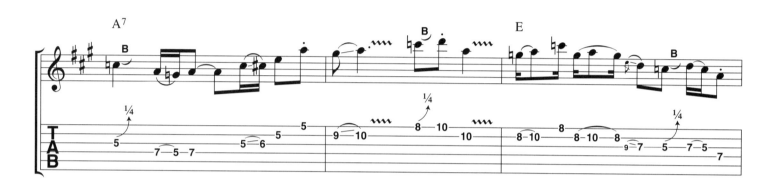

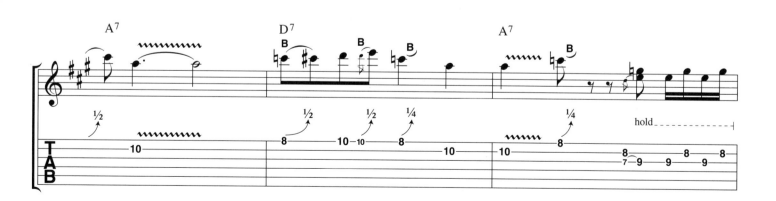

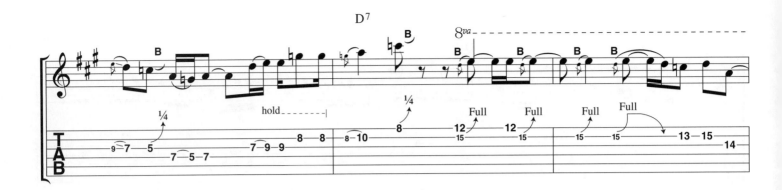

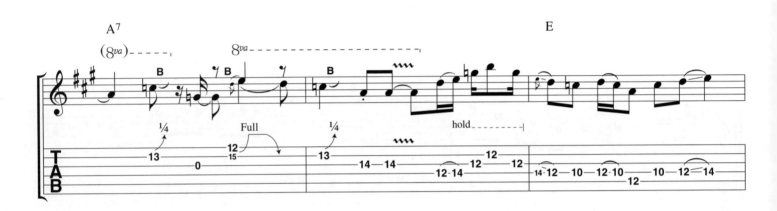

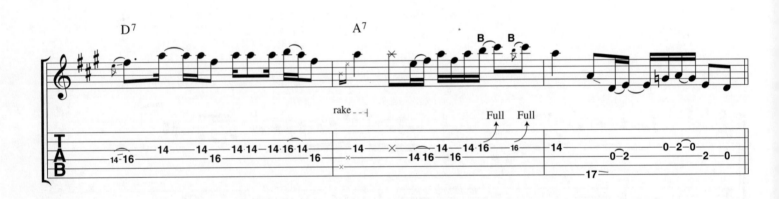

4. Go-ing down_ to Rose - dale,___ take my ri - der by my side.___

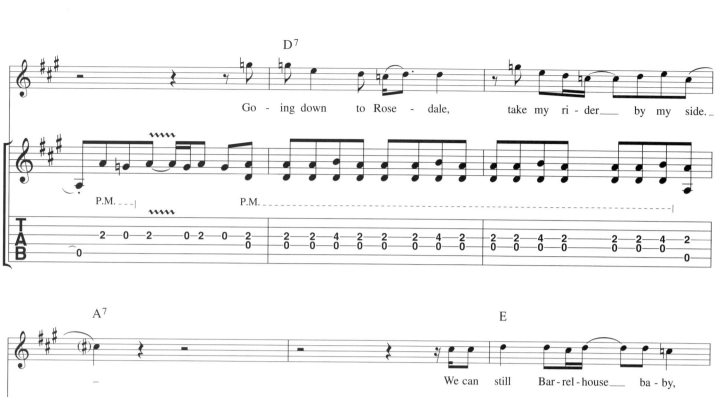

D<sup>7</sup>

Go - ing down to Rose - dale, take my ri - der___ by my side.___

A<sup>7</sup>

E

We can still Bar - rel - house___ ba - by,

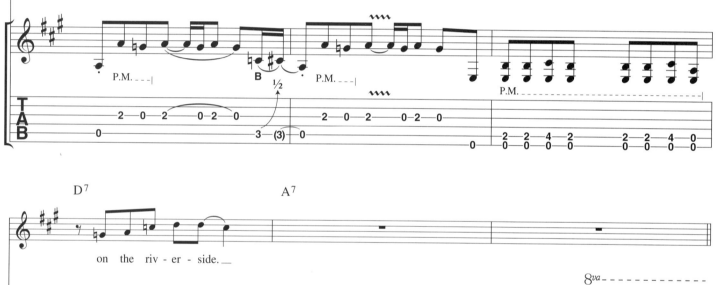

D<sup>7</sup>

A<sup>7</sup>

on the riv - er - side.___

**Solo**

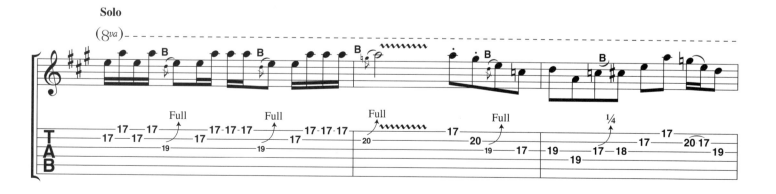

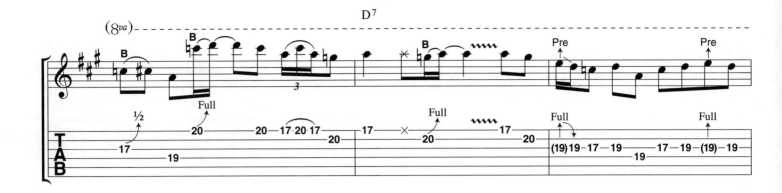

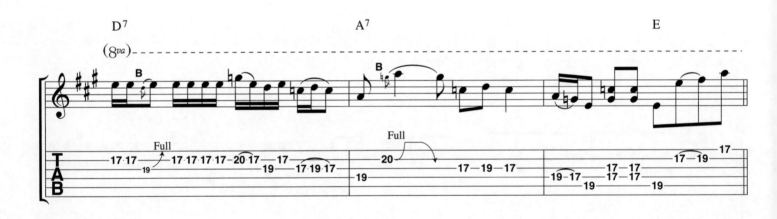

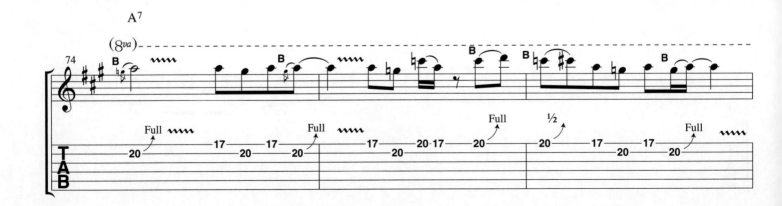

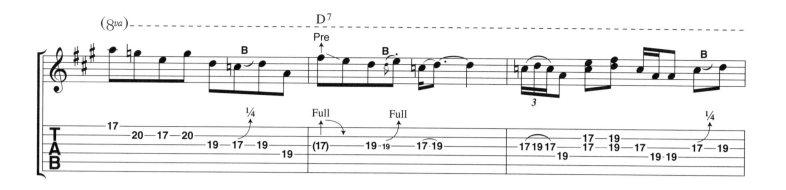

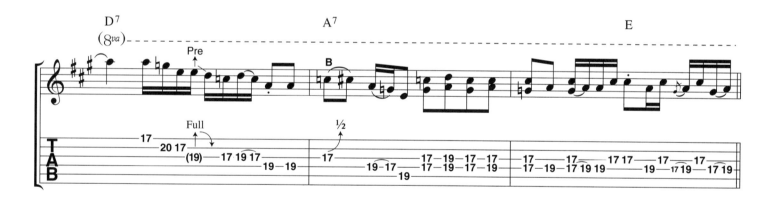

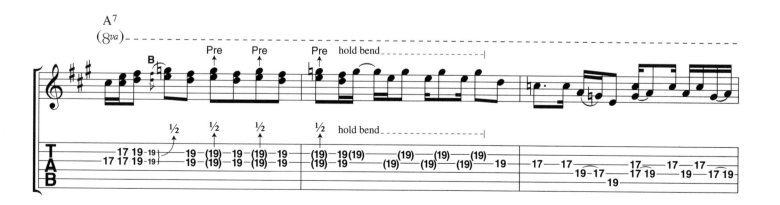

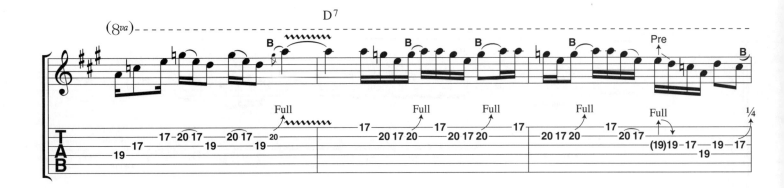

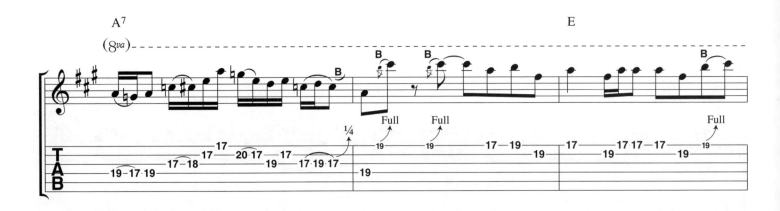

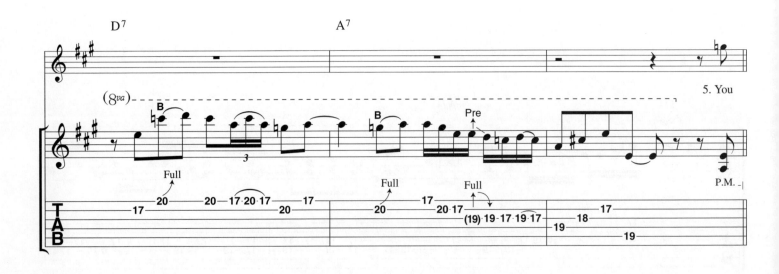

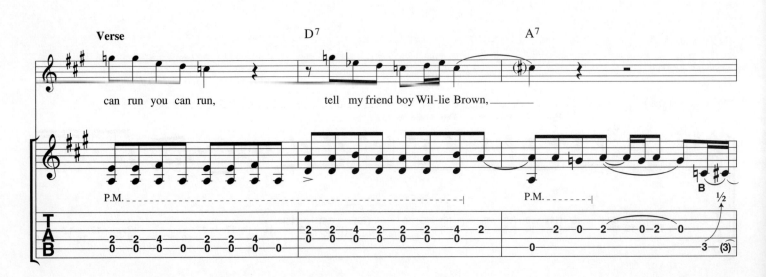

can run you can run, tell my friend boy Wil-lie Brown,

Run_____ you can run,_____ Tell_____ my_____ friend boy Wil-lie Brown.

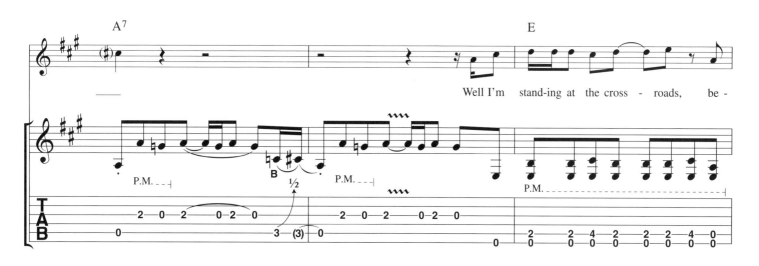

Well I'm stand-ing at the cross - roads, be -

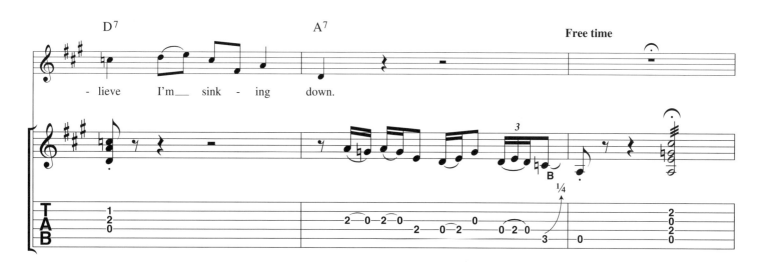

- lieve I'm_____ sink - ing down.

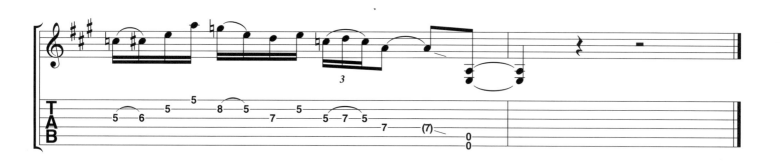

# he don't play nothing but the blues

**Words & Music by Robben Ford**

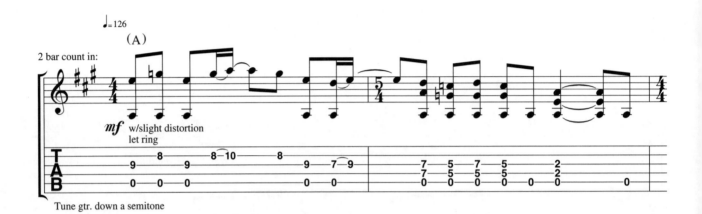

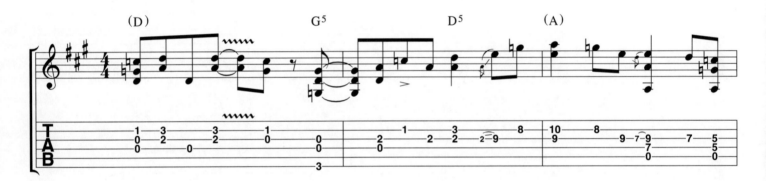

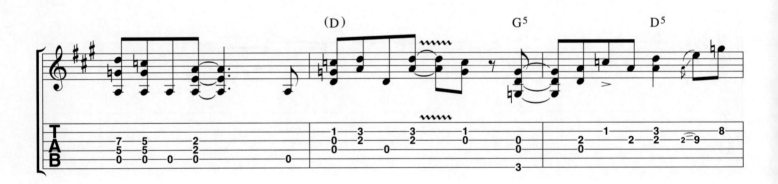

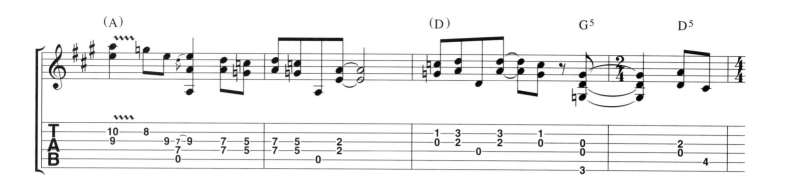

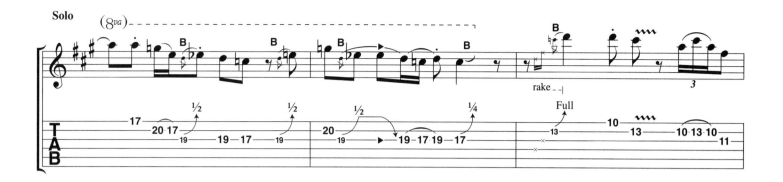

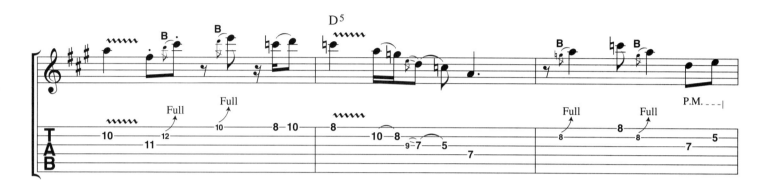

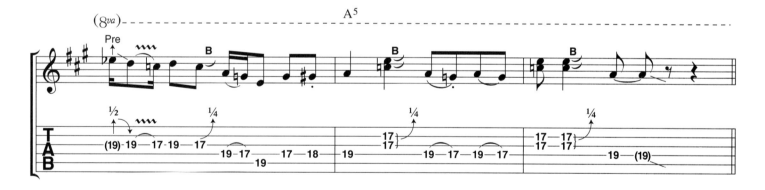

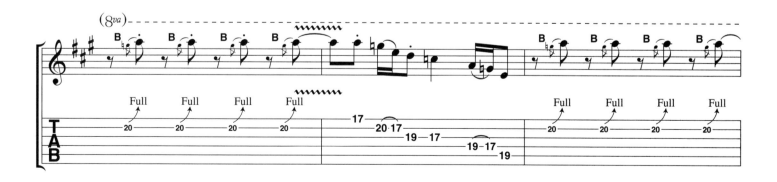

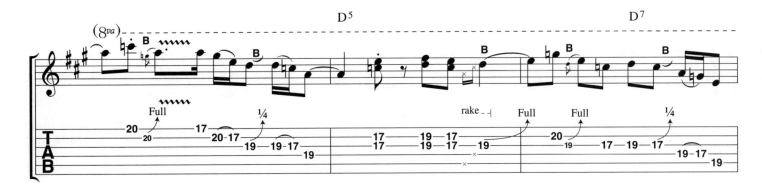

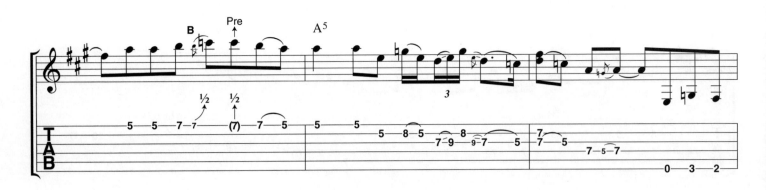

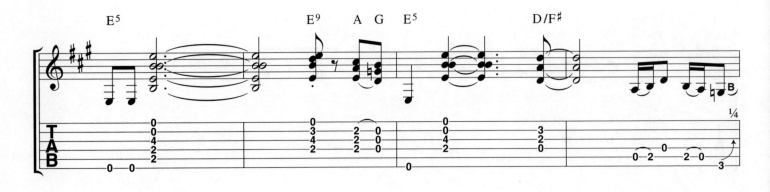

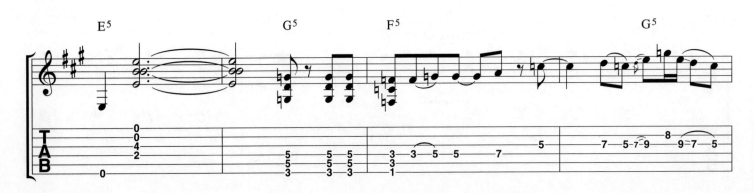

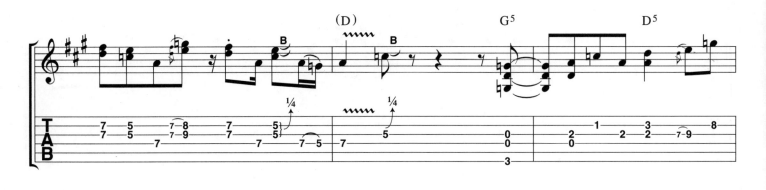

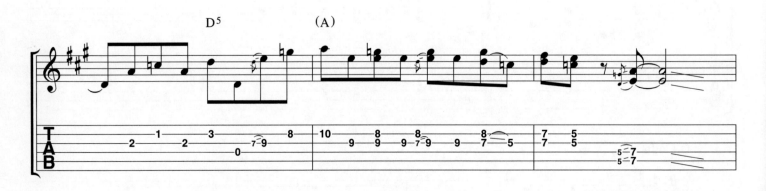
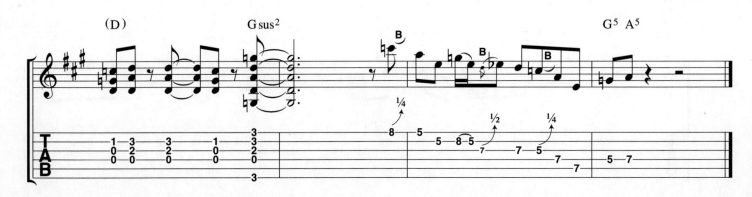

# play *guitar with...*

# *the biggest names in rock*

...eric clapton,
jimi hendrix, john squire, kirk hammett,
mark knopfler, david gilmour, noel gallagher...
*and many more!*

**over
40 *great*
titles**

COMPACT
disc
MCPS

play *guitar with...*

***featuring...***
**Authentic
transcriptions in
standard notation
*and tab***

***plus...***
**Full band
performances on
the CD and separate
backing tracks for you
to play along with**

# play guitar with...
# all these

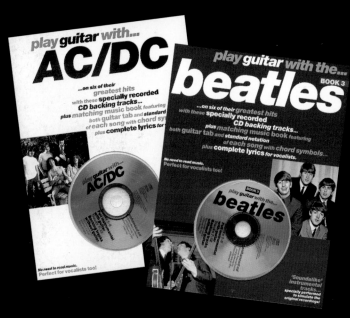

# top bands and artists

**play guitar with... oasis**
...on seven of their greatest hits with these specially recorded CD backing tracks... plus matching music book featuring both guitar tab and standard notation of each song with chord symbols... plus complete lyrics for vocalists.

Seven great songs from 'Definitely Maybe' and 'What's The Story Morning Glory'

No need to read music. Perfect for vocalists too!

**play guitar with... the stone roses** BOOK 2
...on six of their greatest hits with these specially recorded CD backing tracks... plus matching music book featuring both guitar tab and standard notation of each song with chord symbols... plus complete lyrics for vocalists

**play guitar with... paul weller**
...on eight of his greatest hits with these specially recorded CD backing tracks... plus matching music book featuring both guitar tab and standard notation of each song with chord symbols... plus complete lyrics for vocalists.

'Soundalike' instrumental tracks... specially performed to simulate the original recordings.

No need to read music. Perfect for vocalists too!

**play guitar with... the 70's**
...on eight great hits from ac/dc, derek and the dominoes, dire straits, the eagles, free, slade, thin lizzy and wings with these specially recorded... CD backing tracks...
plus matching music book... of each song with chord symbols... plus complete lyrics for vocalists

'Soundalike' instrumental tracks... specially performed to simulate the original recordings.

**play guitar with... the 90's**
...on seven great hits from eric clapton, manic street preachers, metallica, alanis morissette, oasis, pulp and the seahorses with these specially recorded CD backing tracks... plus matching music book featuring both guitar tab and standard notation of each song with chord symbols... plus complete lyrics for vocalists...

'Soundalike' instrumental tracks... specially performed to simulate the original recordings.

No need to read music. Perfect for vocalists too!

## bob marley
includes:
i shot the sheriff
jamming
no woman, no cry
Order No. AM937739

## metallica
includes:
enter sandman
fade to black
the unforgiven
Order No. AM92559

## metallica book 2
includes:
creeping death
seek and destroy
whiskey in the jar
Order No. AM955977

## alanis morissette
includes:
hand in my pocket
ironic
you oughta know
Order No. AM943723

## oasis
includes:
cigarettes & alcohol
morning glory
supersonic
Order No. AM935330

## ocean colour scene
includes:
the circle
the day we caught the train
the riverboat song
Order No. AM943712

## elvis presley
includes:
all shook up
blue suede shoes
hound dog
Order No. AM937090

## pulp
includes:
common people
disco 2000
sorted for e's & wizz
Order No. AM938124

## the rolling stones
includes:
brown sugar
(i can't get no) satisfaction
jumpin' jack flash
Order No. AM90247

## sting
includes:
an englishman in
  new york
fields of gold
if you love somebody
  set them free
Order No. AM928092

## the stone roses
includes:
i am the resurrection
i wanna be adored
ten storey love song
Order No. AM943701

## the stone roses book 2
includes:
fool's gold
love spreads
one love
Order No. AM955890

## suede
includes:
animal nitrate
electricity
we are the pigs
Order No. AM955955

## paul weller
includes:
the changingman
out of the sinking
wild wood
Order No. AM937827

## the who
includes:
i can see for miles
pinball wizard
substitute
Order No. AM955867

## the 60's
includes:
all along the watchtower
  (jimi hendrix)
born to be wild
  (steppenwolf)
not fade away
  (the rolling stones)
Order No. AM957748

## the 70's
includes:
all right now (free)
hotel california
  (the eagles)
live and let die (wings)
Order No. AM957759

## the 80's
includes:
addicted to love
  (robert palmer)
need you tonight (inxs)
where the streets have
  no name (U2)
Order No. AM957760

## the 90's
includes:
everything must go
  (manic street preachers)
love is the law (the seahorses)
wonderwall (oasis)
Order No. AM957770

# play guitar with...
## sample the whole series with
## these special compilations...

**the gold book**
play guitar with...
...on eight great hits from **dire straits,
the beatles, chuck berry,
elvis presley, the kinks,
eric clapton, john lennon**
and **john lee hooker**
with these specially recorded
CD backing tracks...
plus matching music book featuring
both guitar tab and standard notation
of each song with chord symbols
...complete lyrics for vocalists

'Soundalike' instrumental tracks... specially performed to simulate the original recordings

**the platinum book**
play guitar with... **kula shaker,
manic street preachers,
ocean colour scene,
oasis, stone roses,
pulp** and **paul weller**
with these specially recorded
CD backing tracks...
plus matching music book featuring
both guitar tab and standard notation
of each song with chord symbols...
plus complete lyrics for vocalists

'Soundalike' instrumental tracks... specially performed to simulate the original recordings

No need to read music.
Perfect for vocalists too!

### the gold book
**includes eight classic tracks:**
*jailhouse rock (elvis presley)*
*johnny b. goode (chuck berry)*
*layla (eric clapton)*
*sultans of swing (dire straits)*
*the healer (john lee hooker)*
*ticket to ride (the beatles)*
*woman (john lennon)*
*you really got me (the kinks)*
Order No. AM951907

### the platinum book
**includes seven great songs:**
*a design for life*
  *(manic street preachers)*
*cigarettes & alcohol (oasis)*
*disco 2000 (pulp)*
*elephant stone (stone roses)*
*govinda (kula shaker)*
*the changingman (paul weller)*
*the riverboat song*
  *(ocean colour scene)*
Order No. AM951918

**Arthur Dick** has transcribed the music and provided the recorded guitar parts for most of the titles in the play guitar with... series, often bringing in other professional specialist musicians to achieve the most authentic sounds possible!

A session guitarist with over twenty years' experience, he has worked with Cliff Richard, Barbara Dickson, Helen Shapiro, Bernie Flint and Chris Rea among others.

Arthur has played in many West End stage shows, and is in regular demand as a session player for TV, radio, and advertising productions.

He currently lectures on jazz and contemporary guitar at University Goldsmith's College, and works as a freelance production consultant.

**Available from all good music retailers or, in case of difficulty, contact:**

**Music Sales Limited**
Newmarket Road,
Bury St. Edmunds,
Suffolk IP33 3YB.
telephone 01284 725725
fax 01284 702592

**www.musicsales.com**

PUB04634

# hideaway

**Words & Music by Freddie King & Sonny Thompson**

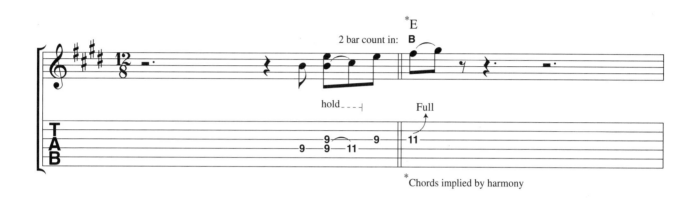

*Chords implied by harmony

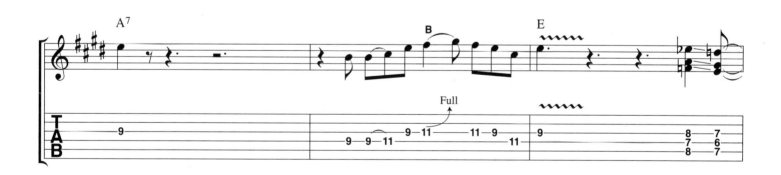

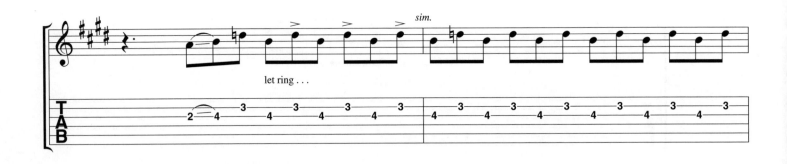

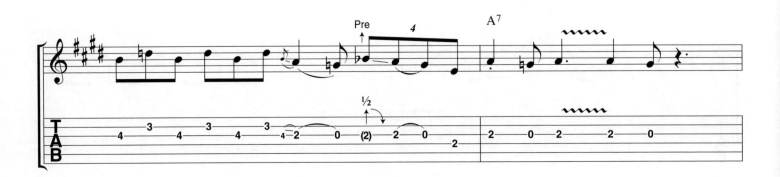

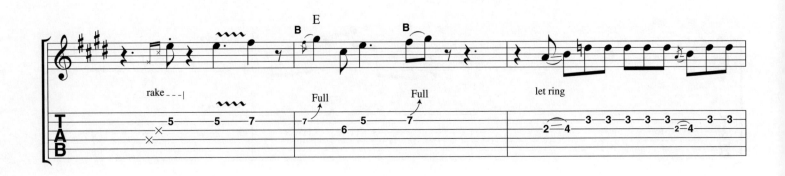

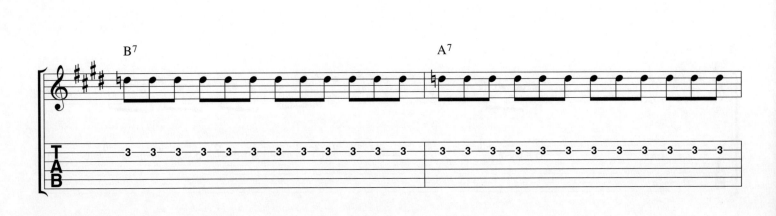

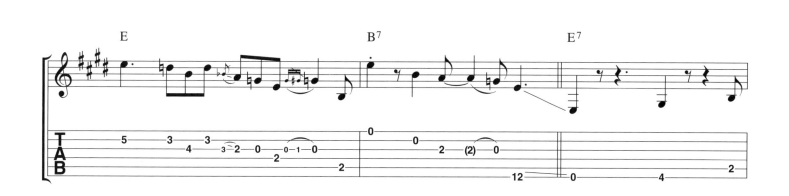
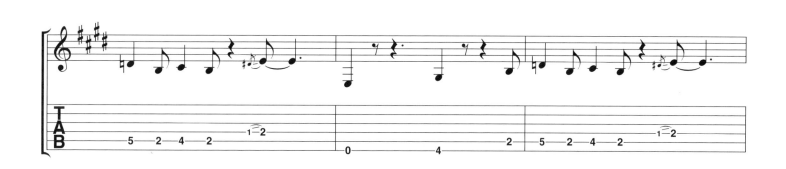

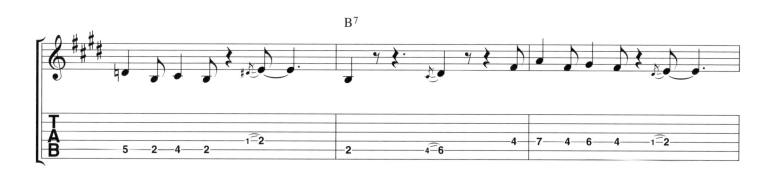

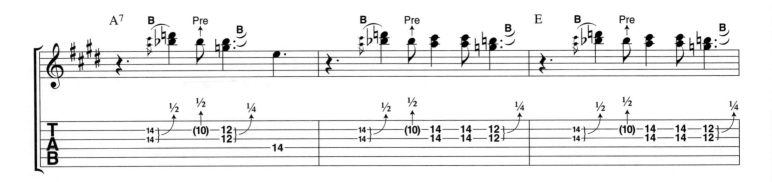

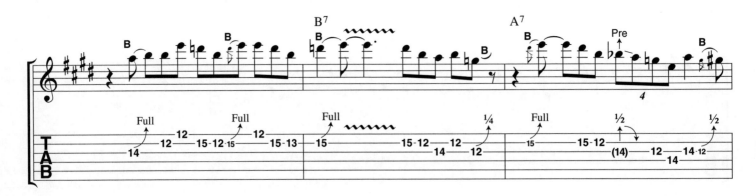

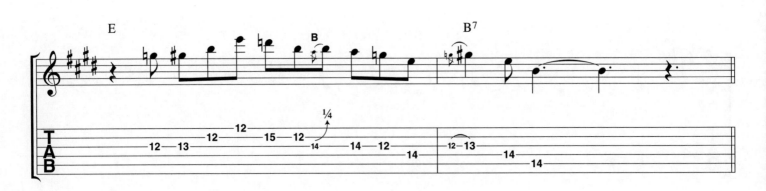

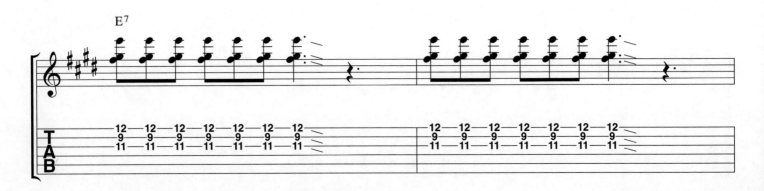

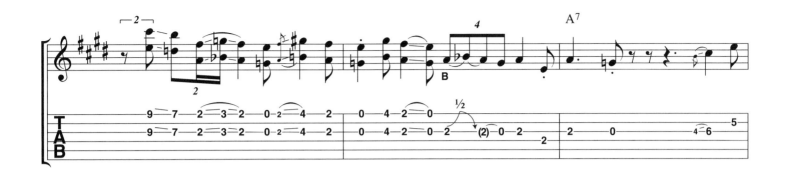

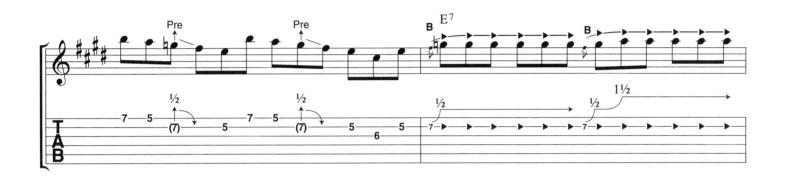

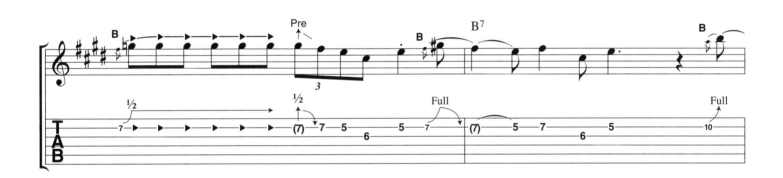

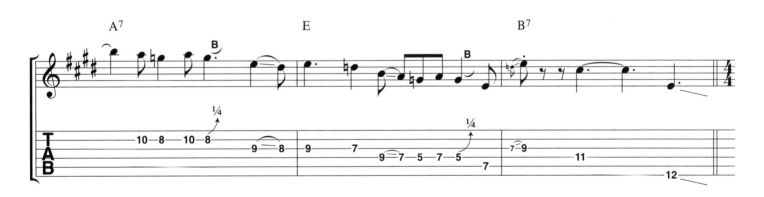

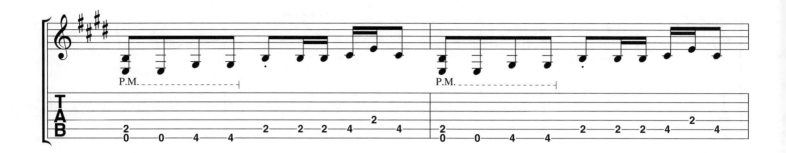

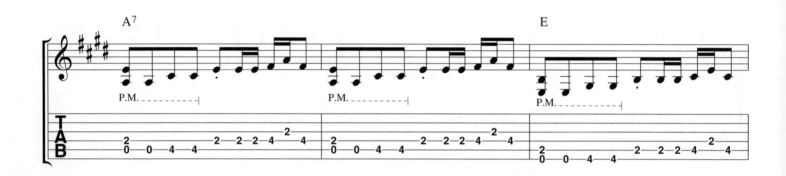

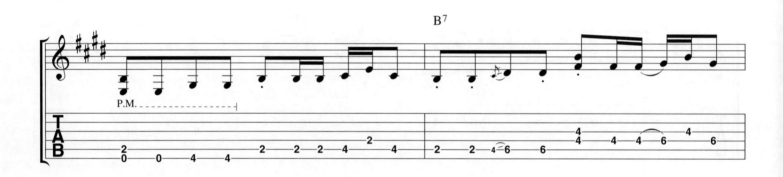

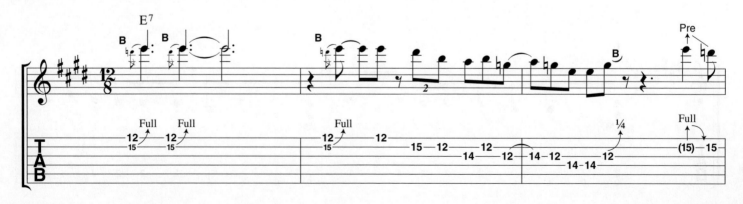

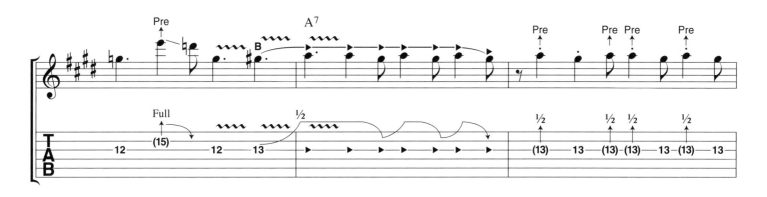

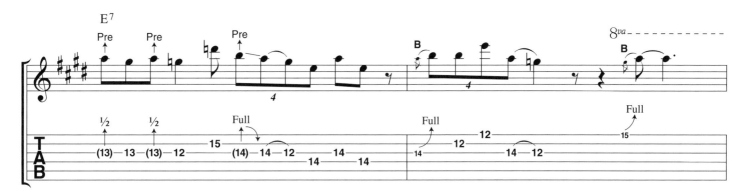

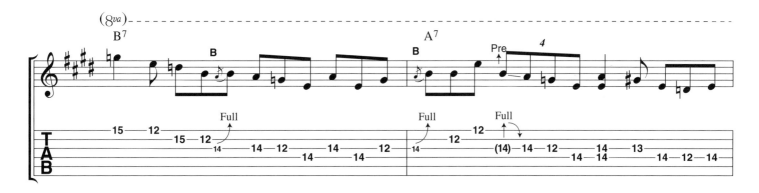

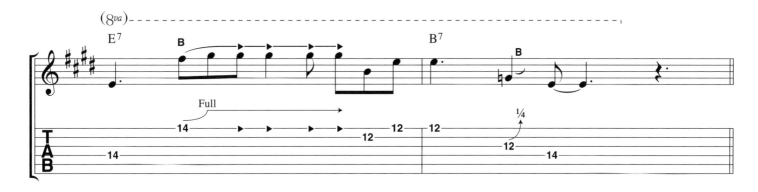

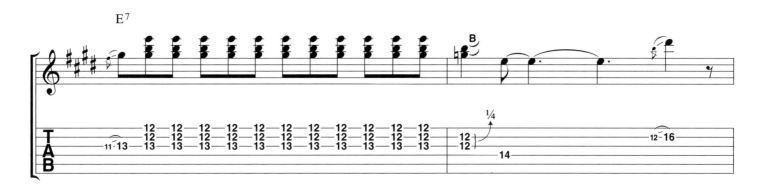

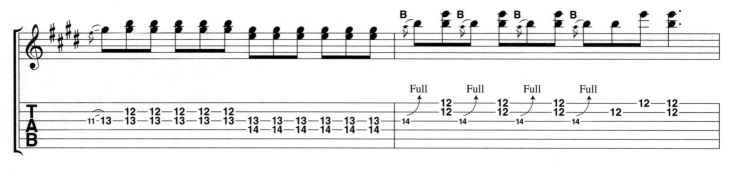

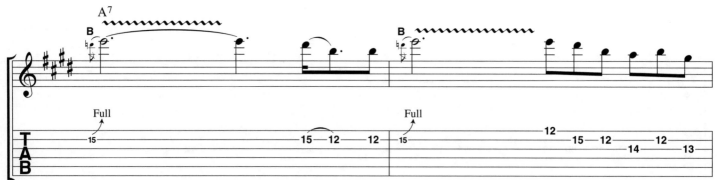

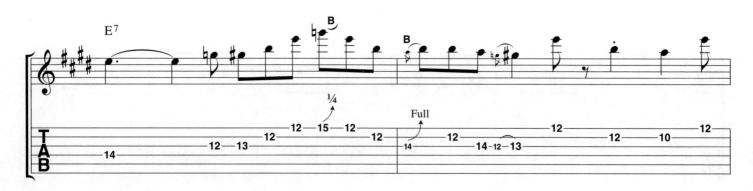

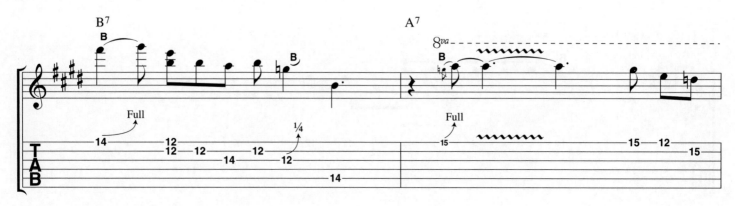

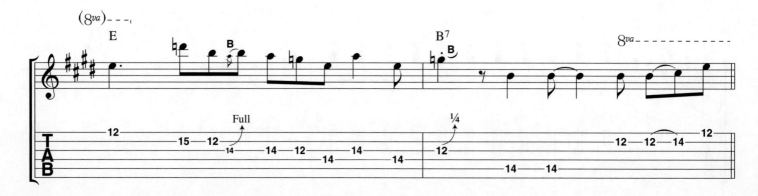

# killing floor

**Words & Music by Chester Burnette**

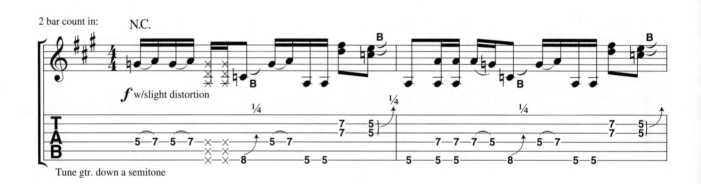

Tune gtr. down a semitone

*Chords implied by harmony

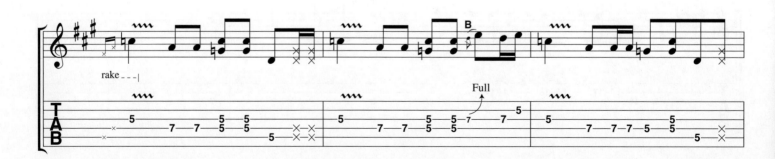

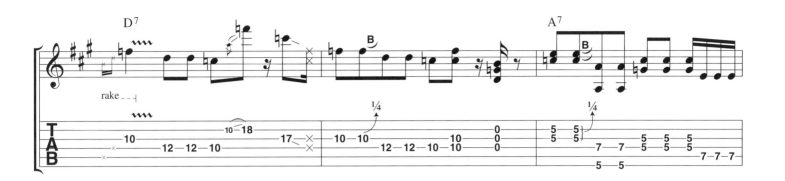

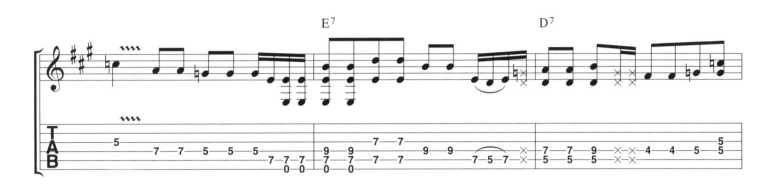

**Verse**

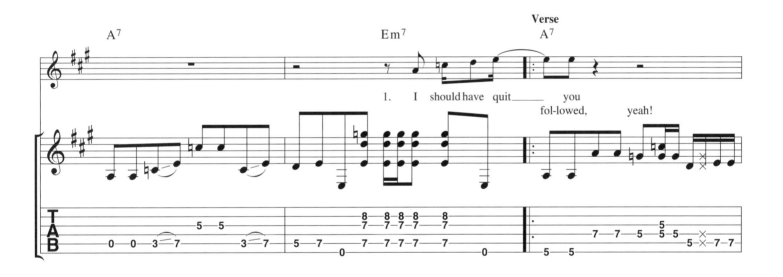

1. I should have quit_____ you
fol-lowed,     yeah!

long_____ time     a - go._____
My_____ first     mind_____

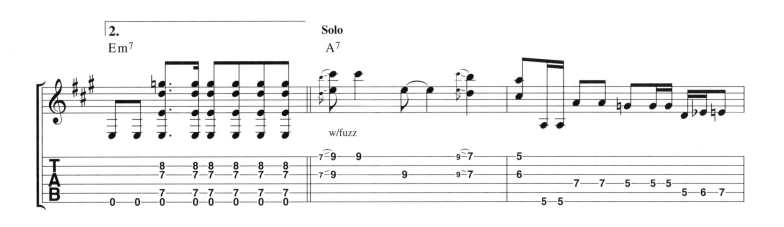

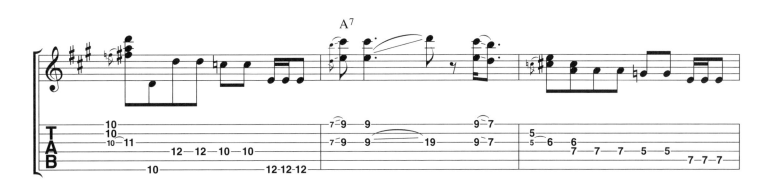

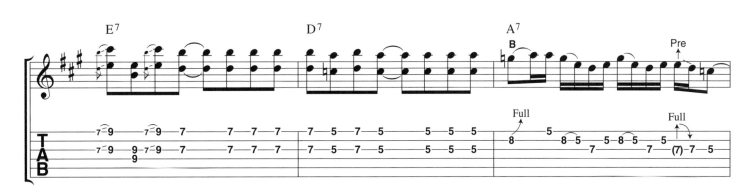

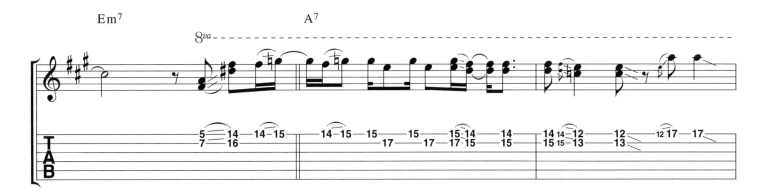

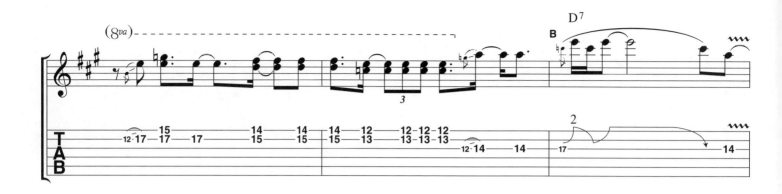

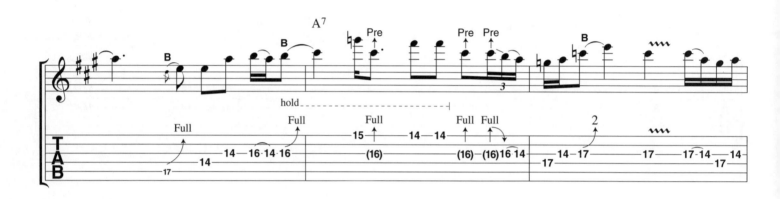

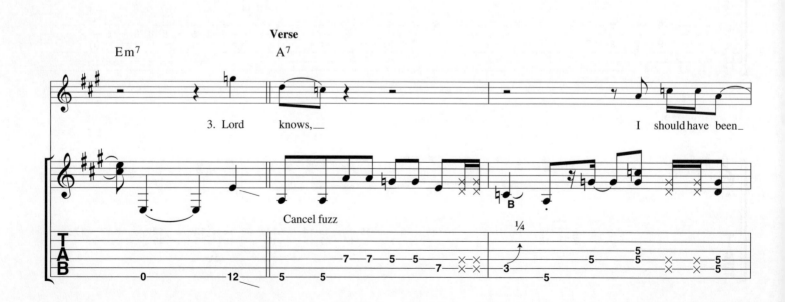

3. Lord    knows,___                            I   should have  been___

Cancel fuzz

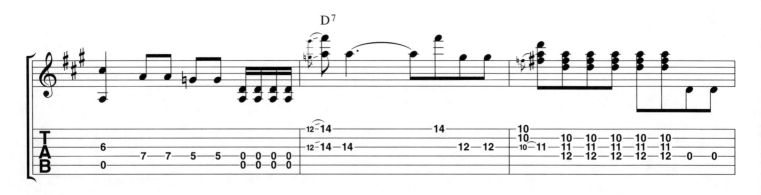

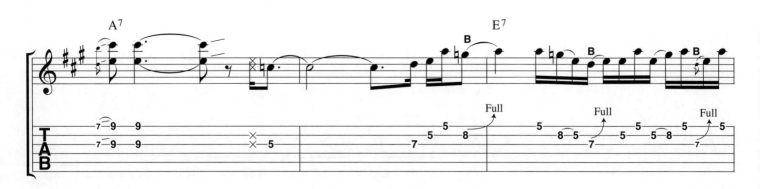

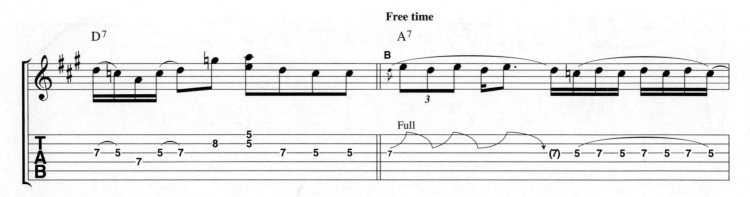

# the stumble

**Words & Music by Freddie King & Sonny Thompson**

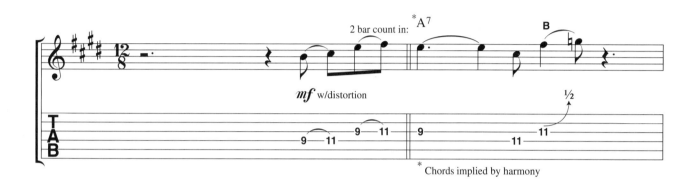

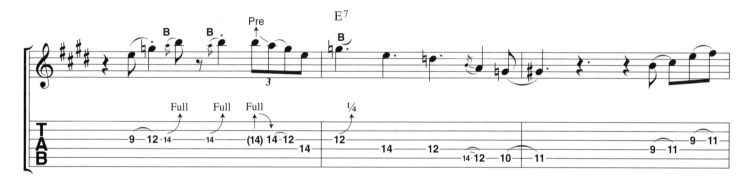

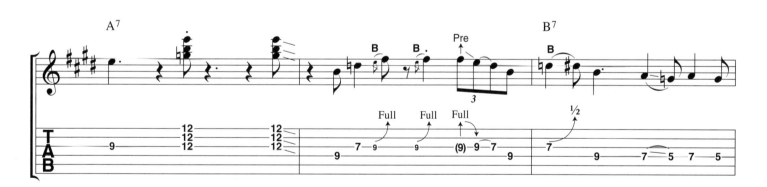

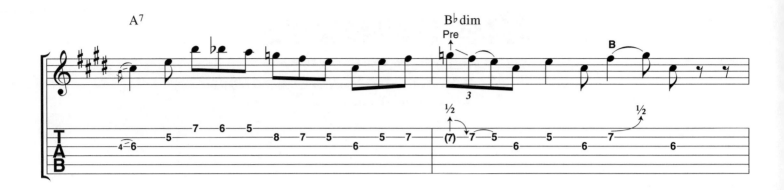

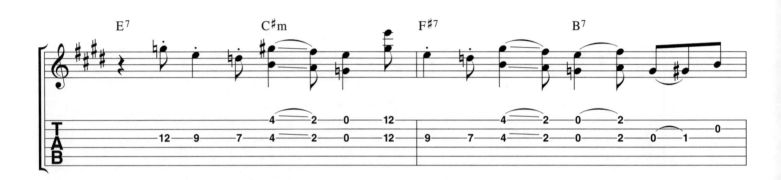

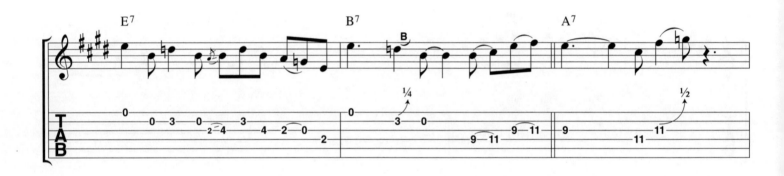

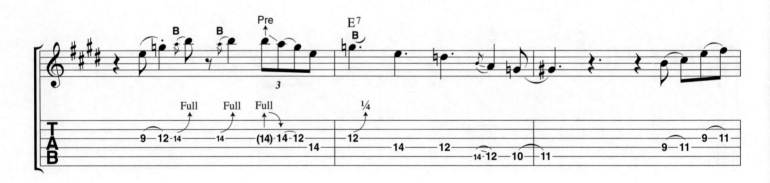

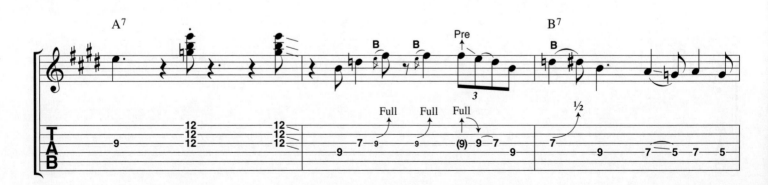

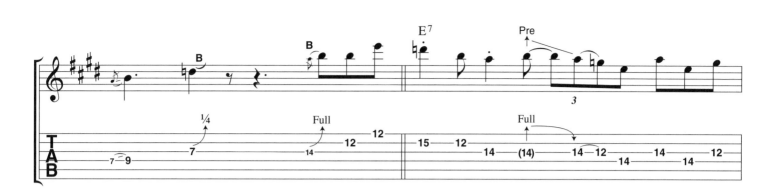

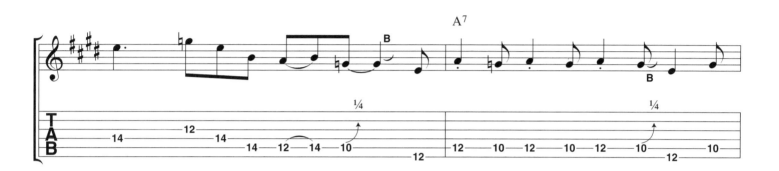

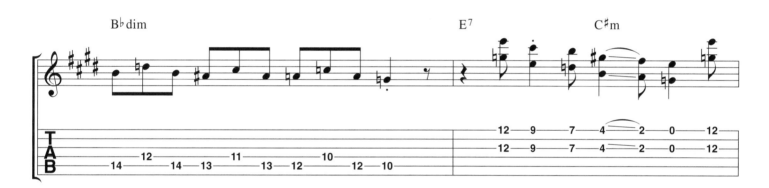

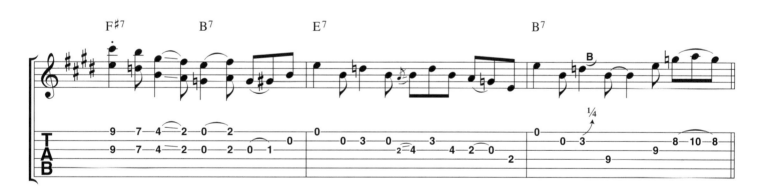

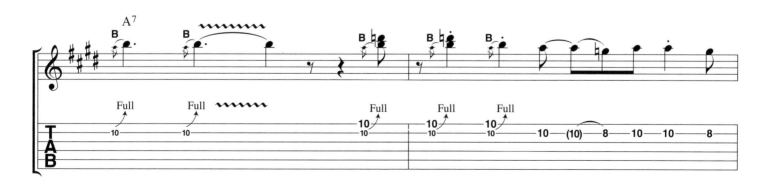

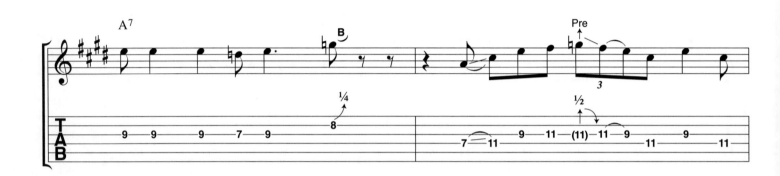

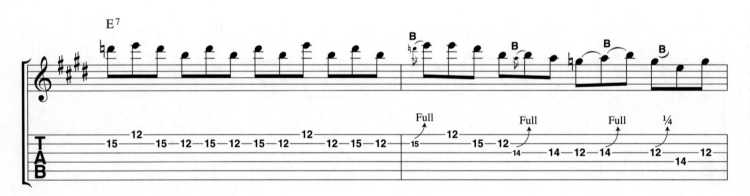

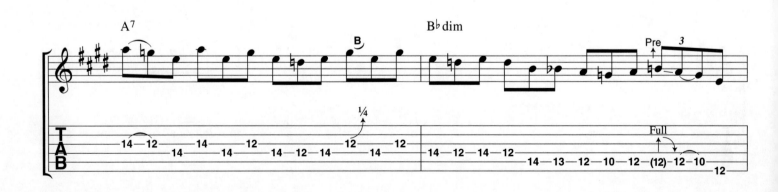

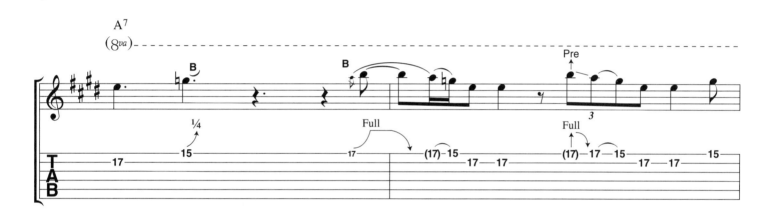

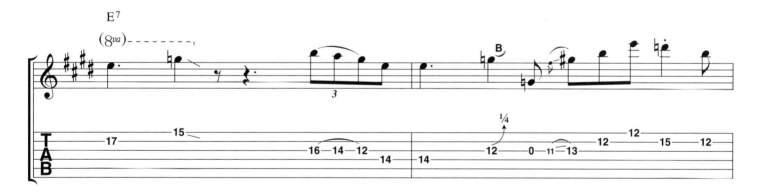

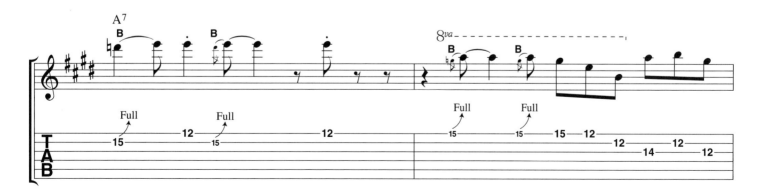

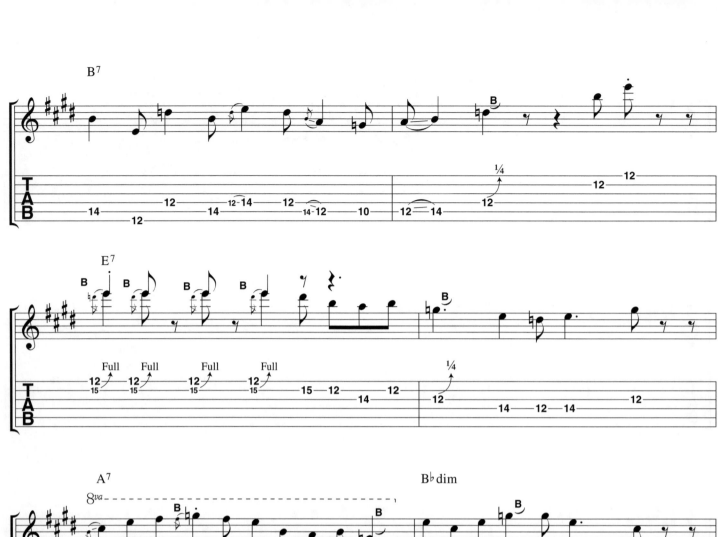

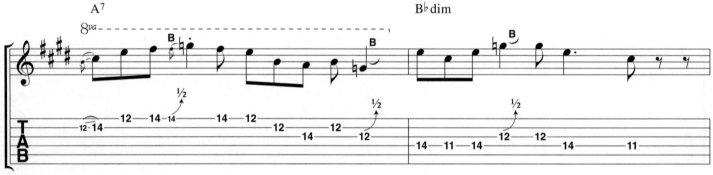

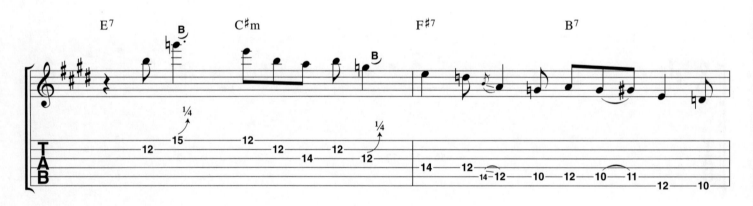

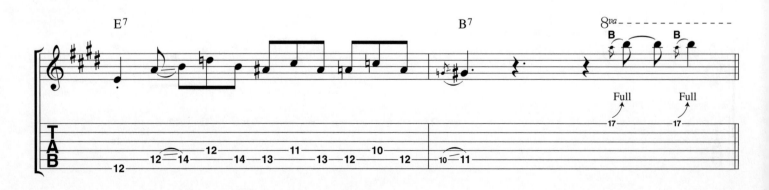

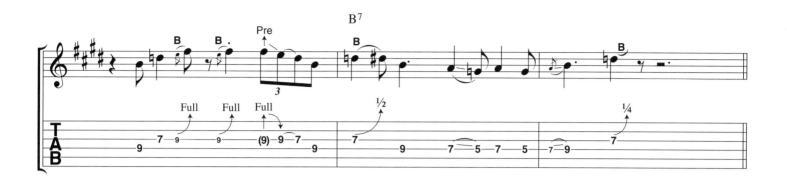

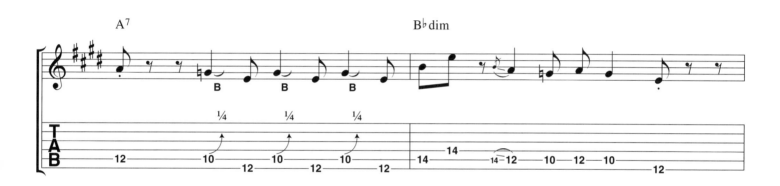

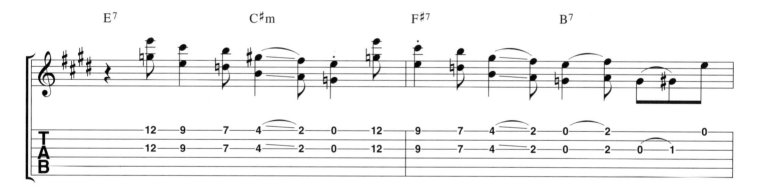

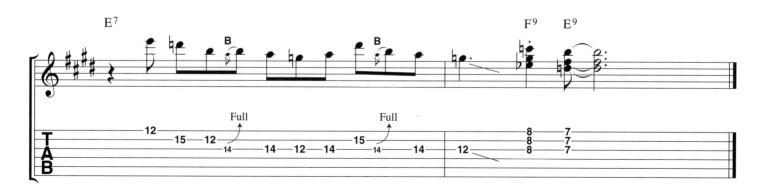

# the thrill is gone

**Words & Music by Roy Hawkins & Rick Darnell**

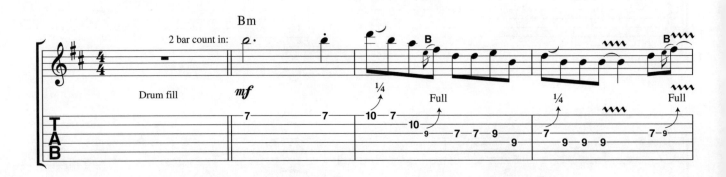

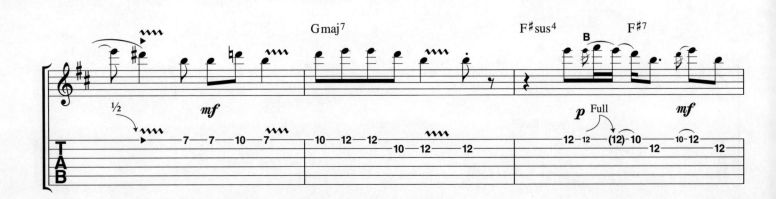

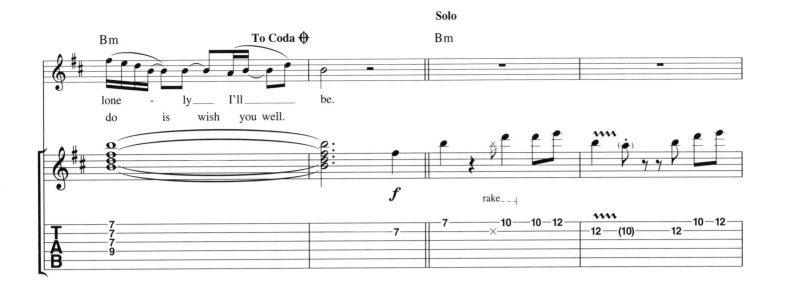

lone - ly___ I'll_____ be.
do   is  wish  you well.

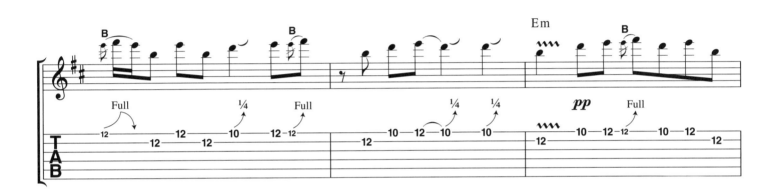

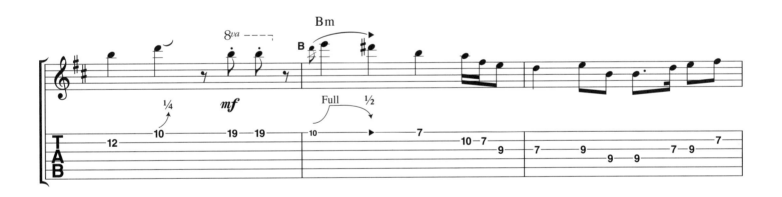

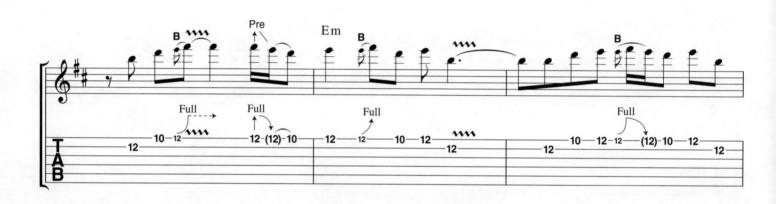

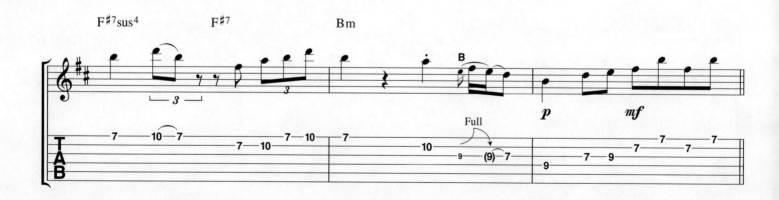

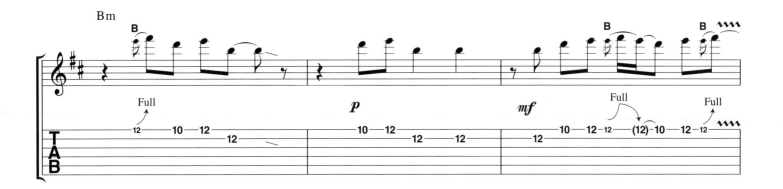

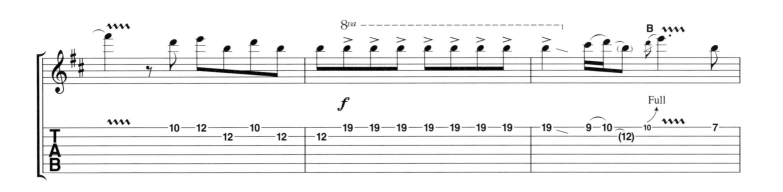

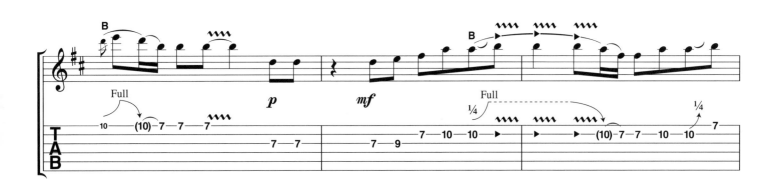

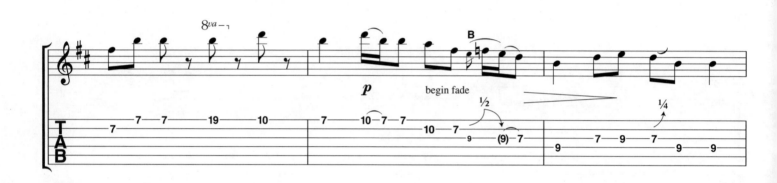

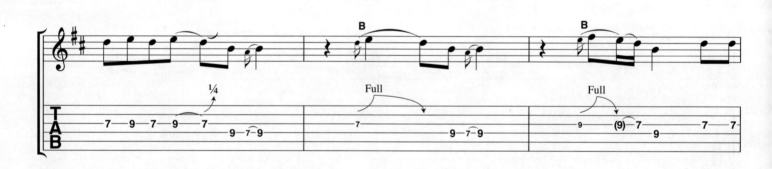